SOVIET
MECHANIZED
FIREPOWER
TODAY
Steven J. Zaloga

Front cover illustration: A battery of SO-152 (2S3) Akatsiya self-propelled 152mm howitzers of the Soviet Central Group of Forces during winter exercises in Czechoslovakia.

Back cover:

Top: An SO-152 (2S3) Akatsiya self-propelled 152mm howitzer on parade in Moscow. (Sovfoto)

Bottom: An SO-122 (2S1) Gvozdika self-propelled 122mm howitzer during the 1981 Zapad manoeuvres in Bylorussia. (Sovfoto)

1. The SU-100 remained in tank destroyer regiments until the early 1960s, by which time it was withdrawn into wartime reserves. Some were still available as late as 1985 when this vehicle took part in the October Revolution parade in Moscow celebrating the end of the Second World War. Interestingly enough, this is a rebuilt SU-100, not an SU-100M. It has been refitted with T-54 starfish wheels, and has had a fuel pump container added behind the commander's cupola. The SU-100's longevity was due to its use of the D-10S 100mm gun, essentially the same armament of the T-54 tank of the time.

SOVIET
MECHANIZED
FIREPOWER
TODAY

Steven J. Zaloga

ARMS AND
ARMOUR

▲ 2

2. The wartime ISU-122S assault gun did not remain in production long after the war, but it remained in service well into the 1960s. This particular vehicle served with the Polish

People's Army (LWP). It was primarily used as a tank-destroyer.

3. Production of the wartime ISU-152 resumed in Leningrad

in 1947 and lasted into the early 1950s. It was considered an assault gun, rather than a tank destroyer, and was used to provide direct fire support for mechanized units. Here, a

vehicle of the Polish LWP is seen during anti-aircraft exercises with a reserve infantry unit.

▼ 3

INTRODUCTION

First published in Great Britain in 1989 by Arms and Armour Press, Artillery House, Artillery Row, London SW1P 1RT.

Distributed in the USA by Sterling Publishing Co. Inc., 2 Park Avenue, New York, NY 10016.

Distributed in Australia by Capricorn Link (Australia) Pty. Ltd., P.O. Box 665, Lane Cove, New South Wales 2066, Australia.

British Library Cataloguing in Publication Data:
Zaloga, Steven J.
Soviet mechanized firepower today. – (Military vehicles fotofax)
1. Soviet Union. Military forces
I. Title   II. Series
355′.00947
ISBN 0-85368-957-1

Line illustrations by the author.

Designed and edited by DAG Publications Ltd.
Designed by David Gibbons; layout by Cilla Eurich; typeset by Ronset Typesetters Ltd, Darwen, Lancashire, and Typesetters (Birmingham) Ltd, Warley, West Midlands; camerawork by M&E Reproductions, North Fambridge, Essex; printed and bound in Great Britain by The Alden Press, Oxford.

The Russians have traditionally called the artillery 'the God of War'. Artillery was always a favoured branch in the Russian Army, and it is no different in the contemporary Soviet Army. This book takes a look at Soviet mechanized artillery since the Second World War with a special emphasis on current equipment.

'The Missile Forces and Artillery' (RViA) is the Soviet name for the artillery arm of the Soviet Ground Forces. The RViA is in turn broken down into organic artillery units and artillery of the Supreme High Command Reserve (RVGK). Organic artillery units are those attached to tank and motor rifle divisions. It was not until the 1970s that a significant fraction of the divisional artillery regiments began to be mechanized with self-propelled howitzers. These include the 2S1 Gvozdika 122mm self-propelled howitzer and the 2S3 Akatsiya 152mm self-propelled howitzer. These tubed artillery weapons are supported by rocket artillery weapons as well. The modern equivalent of the legendary Katyushas of the Second World War is the BM-21 Grad 122mm multiple rocket-launcher. It does not have the precision of gun artillery, but it has an awesome amount of salvo firepower. The most powerful elements of divisional artillery are the nuclear-capable Luna and Tochka ballistic missiles. These provide very long-range fire support for mechanized formations. This book also covers other tracked vehicles associated with Soviet artillery units such as the MT-LBu armoured command vehicle and the MT-LB artillery transporter.

The artillery of the RVGK is the most secret element of Soviet mobile artillery, and the least photographed. In the case of some of these systems, only one or two unclassified photographs are available. These systems are long-range, nuclear-capable weapons, attached to special artillery brigades at Front or Army level. They include such recent additions as the 2S4 240mm self-propelled mortar, the 2S5 152mm SP gun, the 2S7 203mm SP gun and the R-300 (Scud) ballistic missile.

Also included in this book are the anti-aircraft artillery vehicles of the Soviet Ground Forces. These have traditionally been developed by the artillery branch, even though in operational use they come under the control of the Ground Force's Air Defence Force (PVO). The most common vehicle in this category is the dreaded ZSU-23-4 Shilka. A new generation of such vehicles is currently being deployed.

It will be noted that Russian designations have been used when possible for the weapons described in this book, though common Western names are also mentioned. The author would like to thank James Loop, Russ Vaughn, the US Army and the US Defense Intelligence Agency for help in obtaining the photographs used in this book.

▲4 ▼5

4. In 1956, many ISU-152s were rebuilt as the ISU-152K. It included a number of improvements, notably the substitution of a V-54K engine for the older type. This particular vehicle took part in the 1956 fighting in Budapest, and was captured by the Hungarian rebels. Some of the detail changes to the engine deck on the ISU-152K are evident in this view. The ISU-152 was modernized again in 1959 as the ISU-152M, with night vision devices. (Istvan Bathory)

5. The first self-propelled air defence vehicle of the Soviet Army was the ZSU-37, designed during the war. It entered service in small numbers in 1945–6, but its slow turret traverse made it unsuitable to engage modern attack aircraft. It soon disappeared from service.

6. The first major post-war tank destroyer design was the SU-122. It combined the T-54 tank chassis with a new D-49S 122mm anti-tank gun. It was considered highly secret, and photographs of it are very rare. This is a recent Soviet illustration of it.

7. The SU-122 was followed by the SU-130, later known as the IT-130. It consisted of an M-76S 130mm anti-tank gun in a fixed

САМОХОДНАЯ УСТАНОВКА СУ-122

6 ▲   7 ▼

superstructure on the T-62 chassis. It is so secret that the Russians have never released a single photograph of it; this is an artist's impression based on derivative vehicles.

8. The ASU-57 was a tiny air-transportable tank destroyer designed in 1951 for use by the Soviet VDV Air Assault Force. It had to be small enough to fit in a special parachute container carried on the outside of

transport aircraft. It was armed with a 57mm anti-tank gun, in this case the Ch-51M. It was gradually withdrawn from service in the early 1970s as its gun was too small to be effective.

8 ▼

▲9   ▼10   ▼11

9. The ASU-57 was clearly too weakly armed to make an effective tank-destroyer. As a result, in 1956, it was followed by the larger ASU-85 armed with a D-70S 85mm anti-tank gun. Unlike the ASU-57, the ASU-85 was too large to be dropped by parachute, but had to be airlanded by air transport aircraft, which reduced its effectiveness in air landing operations. These ASU-85s belong to the Polish 6th Pomeranian Air Assault Division.

10. The ASU-85 remained in service with Russian and Polish airborne units until the late 1970s. It had never been a really effective tank-destroyer due to the limited performance of its gun. With the advent of the missile-armed BMD airborne assault vehicle, the need for the ASU-85 disappeared.

11. The Kotin design bureau in Leningrad developed a pair of monstrous, nuclear-capable, self-propelled artillery vehicles in the early 1950s. This is the SU-310, which mounted a 310mm gun-howitzer. The chassis was based on components from the IS-3

tanks, and small numbers began to enter service in 1957. A related vehicle, the SU-410, was nearly identical but mounted a long 410mm gun-mortar. These were the only RVGK High Command reserve self-propelled guns for many years.

12. A rear view of the SU-310, the gun pointing over the rear end of the vehicle. Krushchev felt such weapons would be good for little other than parades, and they were soon replaced by rocket artillery, like the Luna series of ballistic rockets.

13. The SU-410 was followed in 1960 by a modified version, the SU-410M, which had this distinctive central driving cab, and a modified loading system. None of these artillery monsters seem to have entered service in any numbers, and they were withdrawn from service in the 1960s.

12 ▲

13 ▼

▲14 ▼15

16▲

14. The SO-122 (2S1) Gvozdika (Carnation) was designed to provide the basic Soviet D-30 122mm howitzer with mobility and armoured protection. Modern artillery location radars are so fast and accurate that artillery must move quickly after firing to prevent destruction by enemy counterbattery fire. This 2S1 is in Polish Army service.

15. A battery of Polish 2S1 Gvozdika preparing to fire. In first-rank Soviet divisions, there is a battalion of 24 Gvozdika in each tank and motor rifle regiment, plus two more in each divisional artillery regiment. This gives each tank or motor rifle division a total of

144 Gvozdika. Some Warsaw Pact armies, like the Polish unit seen here, have not been able to afford such lavish acquisition levels and do not have as many Gvozdika battalions per division.

16. Besides equipping the Soviet Ground Force artillery units, the Soviet Naval Infantry (marines) have begun to modernize with the SO-122 as seen here during exercises of the Naval Infantry Brigade of the Black Sea Fleet in 1987.

17. The SO-122 Gvozdika has a power-assisted loading system as is evident in this view. Soviet mobile artillery systems traditionally receive a 'plant' code-name, hence 'Carnation'

17▲

for this vehicle.

18. At the same time as the 2S1 Gvozdika was being adopted, the Soviet Ground Forces also began acquiring the larger SO-152 Akatsiya (2S3). The Akatsiya is based on a heavier chassis developed from the 2P24 launch vehicle of the ZRK Krug system

(SA-4 Ganef). It is armed with a 152mm howitzer and is capable of a rate of fire of 3 rounds per minute, and a sustained rate of 60 per hour. This particular vehicle participated in the 1981 Zapad manoeuvres in Bylorussia and is of the later production type. (Sovfoto)

18▼

▲19

19. A battery of 2S3 Akatsiya in snow camouflage in operation with the Central Forces in Czechoslovakia. The deployment pattern of the Akatsiya varies, but most Category 1 Soviet tank and motor rifle divisions have a single battalion with eighteen vehicles. The Soviet Ground Forces are currently expanding their artillery holdings in many divisions, and this figure is likely to increase.

20. The East German National People's Army (NVA) is one of the few other Warsaw Pact armies to use the 2S3 Akatsiya. This particular vehicle has its scraper blade fitted on the bow for bulldozing small emplacements.

21. A close-up of the suspension of the Akatsiya. Its relationship to the chassis of the 2P24 launcher vehicle of the SA-4 Ganef is very evident in this view of a Soviet vehicle belonging to a Guards division in the Moscow area.

22. A rear view of a Soviet SO-152 Akatsiya. This is an early production type judging by the configuration of the rear hatches. The small hatches on the hull can be used to load ammunition. Underneath the rear turret overhang is the scraper blade that can be fitted to the front of the vehicle for entrenching. (US Army)

▲20

21▲

22▲

▲23

▲24

▲25

23. An interesting overhead shot of a 2S3 Akatsiya. The turret roof is remarkably bare of hatches or tool stowage. Exit for the crew is through the hull or the side hatch on the right side of the turret.

24. A rare view of the interior of the turret of the 2S3 through the right side turret hatch. The turret crew consists of three: commander, gunner and loader. The loader has a power-assisted loading system because of the weight of the projectiles.

25. A Soviet Akatsiya battalion preparing to fire during the January 1982 Druzhba exercises in Czechoslovakia. Akatsiya batteries are composed of six Akatsiyas, with three batteries per battalion. Overhead is an Mi-24V Hind D attack helicopter, and in the background is an IV13 artillery command vehicle. (Eastfoto)

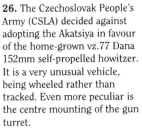

26▲

26. The Czechoslovak People's Army (CSLA) decided against adopting the Akatsiya in favour of the home-grown vz.77 Dana 152mm self-propelled howitzer. It is a very unusual vehicle, being wheeled rather than tracked. Even more peculiar is the centre mounting of the gun turret.

27. A frontal view of the Dana. The Dana was a co-operative effort between Skoda and Tatra, with Skoda providing the gun, and Tatra the chassis. It has not been a total success in service, mainly because of the complexity of its turret's hydraulic system.

27▲

▲28 ▼29

28. Loading ammunition in a vz.77 Dana self-propelled howitzer. For firing, large baseplates have to be lowered to level and steady the vehicle. This makes it much slower to put into operation and move than tracked vehicles like the 2S3. (Chris Foss)

29. A Soviet artillery battalion headquarters in East Germany. The lead IV16 is the version called ACRV M1974-3 (Armoured Command and Reconnaissance Vehicle) by NATO. It is used as the battalion fire direction centre and is commanded by the battalion chief of staff. It can be distinguished by the lack of a rectangular cover midway down the hull which is fitted to both the ACRV M1974-1 and ACRV M1974-2. Behind it is an ACRV-1 (IV13).

30▲

30. A close-up of an East German ACRV M1974-1 (IV13). This is one of the more common versions of the series, and is used as a battery fire direction centre. There is one of these in each 2S1 and 2S3 artillery battery, and it contains the battery commander and his staff. (US Army)

31. A Polish ACRV M1974-1. The MT-LBu uses the same chassis as the SO-122 Gvozdika self-propelled howitzer, with a new superstructure. Like the Gvozdika, it is amphibious. There are many other versions for units other than artillery battlions, including the Dog Ear air defence radar vehicle.

31▼

▲ 32

▲ 33

32. An IV13 of a Polish 122mm self-propelled howitzer battalion. When in action, the ACRV M1974-1 is located near the self-propelled guns it commands. It serves as a communications and command link with the battalion headquarters.

33. A close-up of the turret of an ACRV M1974-1. Both the ACRV M1974-1 and -3 are armed with a 12.7mm DShK heavy machine-gun. To the rear are a pair of Gvozdika.

35▲

35. The AT-PM served in the same role as the MT-LBu and MT-LB in the 1950s. It was related to the ASU-57 tank-destroyer and used a similar chassis. It is seen here towing an 85mm anti-tank gun.

36. A rear view of an AT-PM light artillery transporter. It was typically used to tow anti-tank guns. There was a special version with a reconfigured rear compartment for use as a command vehicle.

34▲

34. The ACRV M1974-2 (IV14, IV15) is the battery and battalion command and observation post. This vehicle is usually forward deployed with whatever unit its parent battery is supporting. Should its battery be supporting a tank regiment, the ACRV M1974-2 will be located near the tank regiment's command vehicles. It is fitted with a laser rangefinder on the right side of the turret. It is armed with a PKT 7.62mm machine-gun instead of the 12.7mm DShK found on the other two command versions.

36▲

▲37

▲38

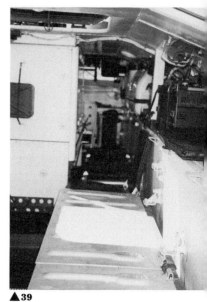

▲39

▼40

37. Since the late 1960s, the Soviet Army has been adopting the MT-LB as its standard armoured tractor. It is used in a wide range of roles, but was originally developed as an artillery tractor to replace the AT-PM. This is an East German MT-LB in its standard role as a tractor for the T-12 100mm smooth-bore anti-tank gun. The Warsaw Pact still uses towed anti-tank guns to supplement anti-tank guided missiles. (US Army)

38. The GT-Mu is a light armoured transporter used to perform various utility roles. It is used in chemical, reconnaissance, electronic warfare, command and ambulance units.

39. An interior view of an MT-LB. This is looking from the rear door forward, down the right side of the hull. A narrow corridor skirts the engine compartment and leads to the machine-gun station in the right front corner of the vehicle.

40. An interior view of the MT-LB showing the left side of the rear troop compartment. The engine is centrally mounted behind the driver and is separated from the troop compartment by this bulkhead.

41. An overhead view of the roof of an MT-LB. The rear troop compartment has two hatches, but the rear section is without hatches to permit loading additional stowage.

42. A close-up of the rear suspension of the MT-LB. The road-wheel is similar, but not identical with that on the older PT-76 tank. Note the scraper against the rear idler which prevents mud from packing up in the wheel and shedding a track.

GLOSSARY

ACRV: Armoured Command and Reconnaissance Vehicle.

Akatsiya: (Acacia), name of Soviet SO-152 (2S3) 152mm self-propelled howitzer.

ASR: *Armata Socialiste Romania*, Army of Socialist Romania.

ASU: *Aviadesantnaya samokhodnaya ustanovka* (airborne mechanized gun), such as ASU-57, ASU-85.

AT-P: *Artilleriskiy tyagach polubronivanniy* (lightly armoured artillery tractor).

BM: *Boyevaya mashina* (combat vehicle), cover name for multiple rocket-launchers.

BMD: *Boyevaya Mashina Desantnaya* (air assault vehicle).

CSLA: *Ceskoslovenska lidova armada* (Czechoslovak People's Army).

FROG: Free Rocket Over Ground, NATO term for the Soviet Luna family of unguided ballistic rockets.

GAZ: *Gorkovskiy Avtomobilniy Zavod* (Gorkiy Automobile Factory).

Gvozdika: (Carnation), Russian name for SO-122 (2S1) 122mm self-propelled howitzer.

ISU: Russian term for an SU (mechanized gun) based on an IS heavy tank chassis.

Luna: (Moon), Russian name for FROG ballistic rocket series, also name for infra-red searchlights on Soviet tanks.

LWP: *Ludowe Wojsko Polskie* (Polish People's Army).

MT-LB: *Mnogotselevoi tyagach legko bronirovanniy* (multi-purpose, lightly armoured tractor).

MT-LBV: *Mnogotselvoi tyagach legko bronirovanniy viezdiekkhod* (all-terrain, multi-purpose, lightly armoured tractor).

NVA: *Nationale Volksarmee* (National People's Army); army of East Germany.

PAZ: *Protivo-atomnaya zashita* (nuclear defence system).

PT: *Plavaushniy tank* (amphibious tank).

PVO: *Protivozdushnoy Oborony* (Air Defence Force), the Russian term for the branch of the armed forces controlling national air defence, formerly (up to 1982) called *PVO-Strany*. The air defence elements of the Ground Forces are called *PVO-Voiska* or *PVO-SV*.

PU: *Punkt upravleniya* (command post); commonly used as a suffix on a vehicle designation, such as BTR-60PU, to indicate a command vehicle.

RGK: *Reserv Glavnogo komandovaniya* (High Command Reserve).

RVSN: *Raketniye Voiska Strategicheskovo Nazcheniya* (Strategic Missile Force), the branch of the Soviet armed forces which controls land-based strategic missiles, split off in 1959–60 from the artillery branch of the Ground Forces. Also sometimes called Strategic Rocket Force.

Shilka: (Awl), Russian name for ZSU-23-4 air defence gun vehicle.

SO: *Samokhodnoye oruzhiye* (mobile gun).

SU: *Samokhodnaya ustanovka*, literally 'mobile unit', usually used as designation for self-propelled artillery. Also SO and SAU.

VDV: *Vozdushno Desantnaya Voiska* (Air Assault Force), the semi-autonomous branch of the Soviet Army responsible for the mobile strategic forces such as air assault divisions.

ZRK: *Zenitniy raketniy kompleks* (anti-aircraft missile system). Sometimes also called ZRK-SD (*srednoye deistvie: medium range*).

SOVIET MECHANIZED ARTILLERY VEHICLES

Soviet designation	SO-122	SO-152		SO-203	SM-240	SO-120
Industrial index	2S1	2S3	2S5	2S7	2S4	2S9
Soviet name	Gvozdika	Akatsiya	Giatsint		Tyulpan	Anona
Crew	4+2	4+2	4+4	4+4	4+5	4
Weight (tonnes)	15.7	27.5	30	40	30	8.0
Length (m)	7.3	8.4	9.5	12.8	8.5	6.02
Width (m)	3.05	3.2	3.2	3.5	3.2	2.63
Height (m)	2.42	2.8	2.8	3.5	3.2	2.30
Ground clearance (cm)	46	40	40	40	40	10–45
Ground pressure (kg/cubic cm)	0.5	0.6	0.6	0.6	0.6	0.5
Gun designation	D-30S	D-20S	2A36		M-240S	
Gun calibre (mm)	122	152	152	203	240	120
Gun type	howitzer	howitzer	gun	gun	mortar	gun/mortar
Depression/elevation (degrees)	−3+70	−4+60	−3+65	−3+65	+45+70	−4+80
Max. rate of fire (min)	5	3	4	2	1	8
Effective rate of fire (min)	5	2	2	1		6
Ammunition stowed	40	46				
Effective range (km)	15.2	17.3	27	30	12.7	
Nuclear capability	no	yes	yes	yes	yes	no
HE projectile weight (kg)	22	40	43.5	100.0	130.7	
Engine designation	YaMZ-23N	V-59	V-59		V-59	5D20
Horsepower	240	520	520		520	300
Fuel stowed (litres)	550	850	850		850	300
Road range (km)	500	500	500		500	500
Max. speed (km/h)	60	60	62		62	60
Amphibious	yes	no	no	no	no	yes
CBR	PAZ+PBZ	PAZ+PBZ	partial	partial	partial	PAZ+PBZ
Max. turret armour (mm)	15	15	−	−	−	23
Max. hull armour (mm)	20	20	20	15	20	18

SOVIET AIR DEFENCE GUN VEHICLES

	ZSU-57-2	ZSU-23-4V1	M-2S6*
Crew	6	4	4
Weight (tonnes)	28.1	20.5	25
Length (m)	8.48	6.49	7.84
Width (m)	3.27	3.08	3.47
Height (m)	2.75	2.63	3.08–3.89
Ground clearance (cm)	43	35	variable
Ground pressure (kg/cubic cm)	0.63	0.52	0.50
Gun	S-68	AZP-23	
Number of guns per vehicle	2	4	2
Gun calibre (mm)	57	23	30
Max. effective range (optical sights, km)	4	2	6
Max. effective range (radar, km)	–	3	5
System reaction time (sec)	5	7	
Burst (rounds per sec)	4	60	
Initial muzzle velocity (m/s)	1000	930	
Max. turret slew rate (degrees per second, elevation/traverse)	20/30	45/80	
Tracking rate (degrees per second, elevation/traverse)	20/30	20/30	
Depression/elevation (degrees)	−3+85	−4+85	−2+85
Ammunition stowed	316	2000**	1000–1400
Max. rate of fire (rpm)	480	4000	
Turret traverse (degrees)	30	45	
Guidance radar	no	Gun Dish	Hot Shot
Radar frequency	no	J band	
Radar range (km)	no	20	15
Max. vehicle armour (mm)	14	9.4	15
Engine type	V-54	V-6R	V-59
Horsepower	520	280	520
Fuel stowage (litres)	640	250	
Max. road range (km)	400	260	250
Max. speed (km/h)	50	44	45
CBR protection	no	PAZ+PBZ	PAZ+PBZ
Radio	R-113	R-123	R-123M

*Provisional Data
**Initial ZSU-23-4 versions carried only 1000 rounds

43. A Bulgarian unit on exercise with an MT-LB. This particular version is a common artillery ammunition type, and has a large pannier on the roof to permit ammunition crates to be stowed.

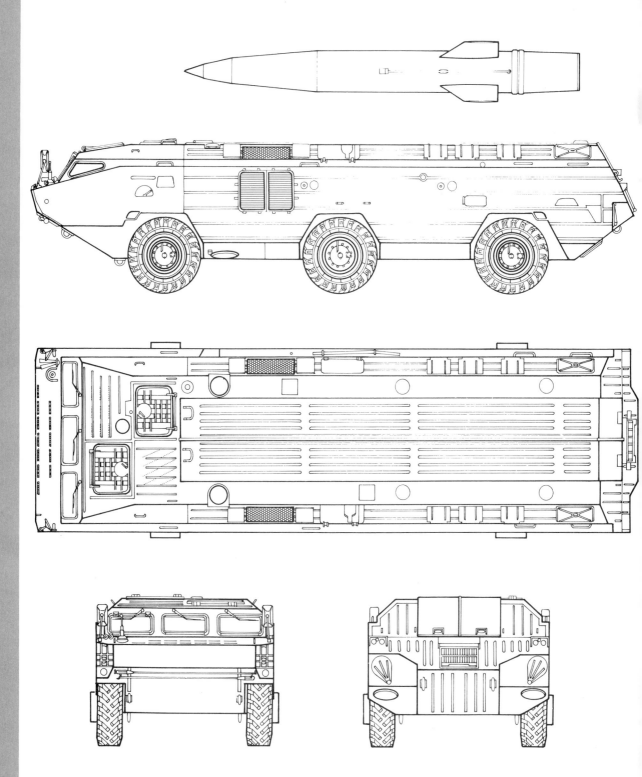

SS-21 SCARAB TACTICAL BALLISTIC MISSILE SYSTEM

2S6 AIR DEFENCE GUN/MISSILE VEHICLE

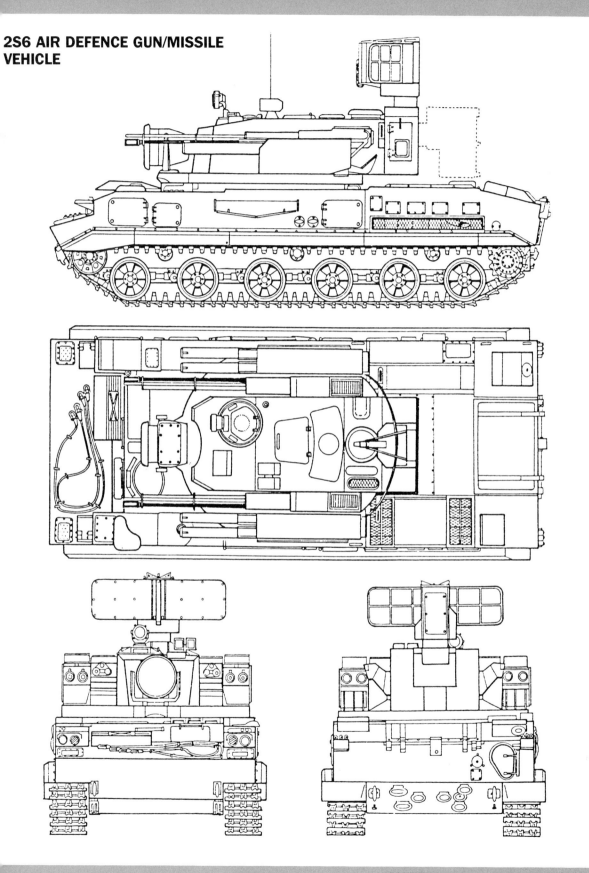

▲44

▲45 ▼46

▲47

44. The 2S4 Tyulpan self-propelled 240mm heavy mortar is one of the least known of the family of self-propelled guns introduced by the Soviet Ground Forces in the late 1960s. It is based on the same chassis as the 2S3 152mm self-propelled howitzer. This is a US Army illustration showing the vehicle in travel configuration with the mortar tube stowed. The mortar is a modified version of the M-240. This poor view of a pair of Czech 2S4 mortar vehicles is one of the few photographs that have appeared of this elusive armoured vehicle. It shows the M-240 mortar in the firing position, pointed over the rear end of the vehicle. The hull contains a power rammer to assist in loading the ammunition. The 2S4 are employed by special High Command Reserve (RVGK) artillery brigades.

45. A rear view of the modified base plate of the 2S4. Its enormous size is evident when noting the height of the vehicle commander nearby.

46. As in the case of the 2S4, there are few photographs yet of the 2S5 Giatsint (Hyacinth) 152mm self-propelled gun. This is based on the same chassis as the 2S3 and 2S4 self-propelled artillery vehicles. This US Army illustration shows a trainload of Giatsint with the Group of Soviet Forces-Germany (GSFG). These artillery vehicles serve in artillery brigades at army or front level, not in divisional artillery formations – hence their rarity. (DoD)

47. One of the most massive of the new generation of self-propelled artillery is the 2S7 self-propelled 203mm gun. It is based on a new heavy chassis, using components from the T-80 tank. This is a vehicle of the Czech CSLA. In Soviet service, these vehicles serve in RVGK heavy artillery units. For example, a front artillery division might have a battalion of 24 of these vehicles.

48. Some idea of the size of the 2S7 can be gathered from this front view of a Czech vehicle with its gun tube near full elevation.

49. This side view of a 2S7 gives a good idea of its enormous size. It is capable of firing a 220lb projectile at least 30km. These guns are located in special front-level heavy artillery brigades. (DoD)

48 ▲ 49 ▼

50. This rear view of a 2S7 shows the control platform for the ammunition loading system. Because of the weight of the shells, there is a hydraulic assist at the rear for loading.

51. To date, this is the only type of vehicle known to use this new chassis. This is the largest self-propelled artillery vehicle in service today, exceeding the size and performance of the American M110A2.

52. The smallest of the new Soviet self-propelled artillery vehicles is the 2S9 Anona gun/mortar vehicle. This vehicle is used by the VDV Air Assault Forces, and can be para-dropped like the BMD on which it is based.

53. The 2S9 has a crew of four—two in the turret and two in the hull. The weapon is a unique gun/howitzer, capable of firing a projectile at a high elevation.

▲ 50

▲ 51

▲ 54

54. The Anona has an unusual configuration in that the commander sits to the left of the driver, rather than in the turret.

55. Combat in Afghanistan has led to some unique improvisations. This 2B9 Vasilyok 82mm towed auto-

mortar unit has removed the wheels from its auto-mortars and mounted them on the roof of its MT-LB tractors.

56. The ZSU-57-2 entered service in 1950, and was the first Soviet anti-aircraft artillery vehicle to be manufactured in significant numbers since the

Second World War. It was armed with twin S-68 57mm guns, a derivative of the standard S-60 57mm divisional air defence gun also entering service at the time. It was based on a lightened T-54 tank chassis. This particular vehicle is in Polish service.

57. The ZSU-23-4 Shilka (Awl) was developed in the late 1950s to replace the ZSU-57-2. The main shortcoming of the ZSU-57-2 was that it relied entirely on optical fire control, which proved inadequate against fast attack aircraft. This Polish ZSU-23-4 is from the initial production version which entered service in 1965.

▼ 55

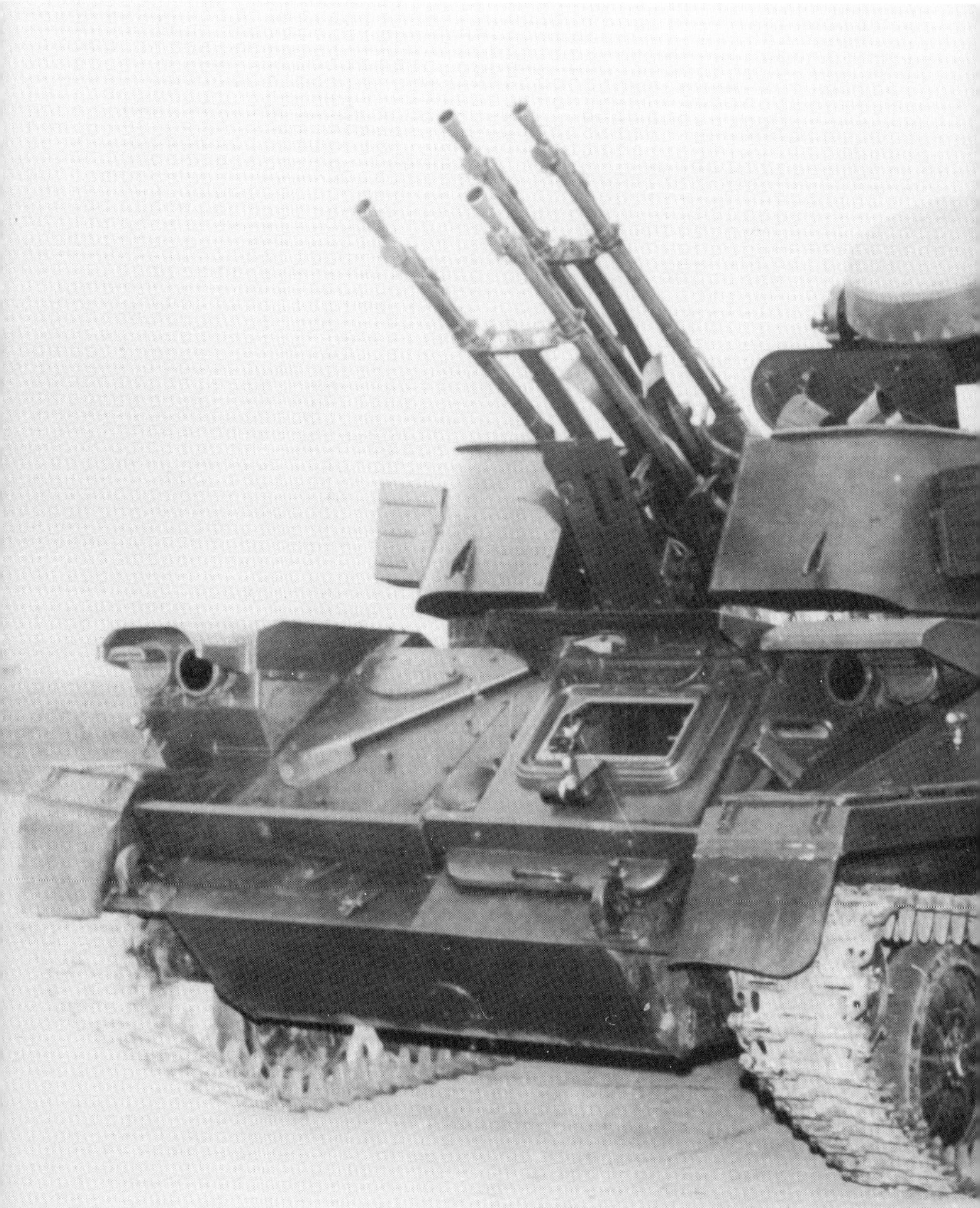

59 ▲

60 ▲

58. The Shilka was plagued by a number of design flaws, and there were many attempts to correct the situation. This is the ZSU-23-4V which entered service in 1968 in an attempt to solve some of the electronics problems.

59. Another view of the ZSU-23-4V of the later production batch showing slightly different cooling vents on the left turret side. One of the main problems of the early Shilka was the congestion of tube electronics which led to overheating and system failure.

60. A rear view of the ZSU-23-4V. The Shilka was developed by the Astrov design bureau, and was based on a chassis essentially similar to that used with the ASU-85 airborne tank-destroyer and 9M9 Kub (SA-6 Gainful) air defence missile vehicle.

61. A right side view of the ZSU-23-4V. The turret venting arrangement on the Shilka is asymmetrical as is evident in this view. The vehicle radar, called 'Gun Dish' in NATO, is seen here pointing to the rear.

62. A frontal view of a ZSU-23-4V, currently preserved at the Soviet Army Engineer Museum in Leningrad, with the quad 23mm cannon near full elevation. In the background is an RZ-25 (Griffon) anti-ballistic missile.

63. A close-up of the rear deck of a ZSU-23-4V. The rear turret panel gives access to the radar electronics.

64. A close-up of the quad AZP-23 cannon on a ZSU-23-4V. The extensive tubing is for a liquid cooling system for the barrels; the chutes are for expended brass casings. This system has a maximum rate of fire of 60 rounds per second, which tends to lead to very rapid barrel deterioration.

▲65

▲66

65. A close-up of the Gun Dish radar on the ZSU-23-4V. This is a J-band radar with a range of about 20km. It is used initially for sector search and target acquisition, and can then be switched to target tracking for fire control purposes.

66. In 1972, the ZSU-23-4V1 version appeared which has been the most common model of the Shilka. It is most easily distinguished by the larger turret panniers which permitted an increase in ammunition stowage. Here, the crew is loading the ammunition panniers of a ZSU-23-4V1. There are three standard rounds of ammunition for the 23mm gun: an armour piercing-incendiary, a high explosive-fragmentation and a high-explosive-incendiary round.

67. A rear view of the Gun Dish radar on a ZSU-23-4V1. This is a J-band radar, and it has gone through a number of improvements since the initial models. (US Army)

68. In 1977, a new version of the Shilka was first displayed in Moscow, called the ZSU-23-4M. It is distinguishable by the reconfiguration of the side panniers and by changes in the venting ports and access panels on the roof. It incorporated extensive internal improvements.

69. The replacement for the ZSU-23-4 began entering service in 1986–7. Its Soviet designation is 2S6, and it is called the SPAAG M-1986 by NATO. As no photographs of the vehicle have yet been released, a model is shown here. It is armed with twin 30mm automatic cannon, and equipped with a more sophisticated radar system (called Hot Shot by NATO) than the Shilka. (Author)

▲67

▲70

▲71

70. The BM-25 was the largest Soviet multiple rocket-launcher of the 1950s. It is based on the KrAZ-214 heavy truck, with six launch rails. The rockets have a maximum range of about 55km. It is no longer in widespread service.

71. The BMD-20 was another long-range multiple rocket-launcher, based on the ZiL-151 truck. The rockets had a range of about 19km, and there were four rails per vehicle. It is no longer in widespread service.

72. The BM-21 Grad (Hail) became the standard Soviet multiple rocket-launcher in 1964. It was intended to replace the wide range of older multiple rocket-launchers in service at the time. It is fitted with 40 tubes for 122mm M-21-OF rockets. This is a Grad of the Romanian Army.

73. The BM-21 is in widespread service around the world. This particular BM-21 Grad is seen in Iranian Army service in the 1970s.

▲74

▲76

74. The BM-21V Grad-P is an airborne forces version of the Hail family. It is mounted on a GAZ-66B light truck, and carries fewer launch tubes than the basic BM-21.

75. The Czech CSLA decided against adopting the BM-21 in favour of a local derivative, the RM-70. This is based on an armoured Tatra 813 truck. It uses a similar launcher assembly, but is also fitted with a rapid-reload system mounted in the centre of the vehicle.

▲75

76. The RM-70 is a good deal larger than the BM-21, and has somewhat less cross-country mobility. This is offset by its armour protection for the crew, and by its ability rapidly to reload for a second salvo.

77. The latest Soviet multiple rocket-launcher is the BM-27 Uragan (Hurricane) seen here in this poor photograph. It is based on the BAZ-135L4 chassis and is armed with 16 tubes for the 9M27 220mm rocket.

78. The Luna rocket, called FROG-1 by NATO, was the first large mobile artillery rocket adopted by the Soviet Ground Forces after the war. It is mounted on a modified IS-2 heavy tank hull.

These are East German NVA RM-70s.

▲79   ▲80   ▼81

79. An overhead view of the FROG-1 launcher. This rocket had a range of about 32km. It was cumbersome and was soon replaced by the FROG-3 family based on the lighter PT-76 chassis.

80. The Luna-2, called FROG-3 by NATO, was mounted on a modified PT-76 light tank chassis. It had a maximum range of about 35km, and was usually armed with a nuclear warhead. These are Romanian ASR launchers.

81. In 1965, the Soviet Ground Forces began receiving a new version of the Luna system, called Luna-M. This has become the standard version of this divisional rocket artillery system and is called FROG-7 by NATO. The launch vehicle, designated 9P113, is based on the BAZ-135L4 truck. The new missile, designated 9M21, or R-70, comes in several versions.

82. A Luna-M battery in the field. The Luna-M has considerably better range than the earlier FROGs, with a maximum range of 70km. This particular rocket is one of the improved derivatives with small spoiler fins at the rear to give the a reduced minimum range.

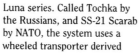

▲83

83. In the early 1980s, the Soviet Army began to receive a new family of short-range ballistic missiles to replace the Luna series. Called Tochka by the Russians, and SS-21 Scarab by NATO, the system uses a wheeled transporter derived from the BAZ-5937 chassis used with the SA-8 Gecko air defence missile system.

▲85

84. An overhead view of the SS-21 Scarab launcher vehicle. It is not yet clear if the missile is launched at an angle as seen here, or fired from a vertical position.

85. An SS-21 in Soviet service. The SS-21 launcher vehicle permits the missile to be carried in an entirely enclosed · compartment, offering better protection in bad weather.

86. The heavier counterpart of the FROG is the SS-1b Scud A, designated R-11 by the Russians. This early version of the Scud series was mounted on a modified IS-2 heavy tank chassis. It was replaced in the 1960s by the R-17 missile, which used a slightly modified version of the IS-2 launcher.

84▲   86▼

▲87

87. The R-17 was eventually mounted on a modified MAZ-543P chassis to give the system better mobility. The R-17 is used by special missile artillery brigades at front and army level. It is currently designated R-300 by the Soviet Ground Forces. The launcher vehicle is popularly called Kashalot (Sperm Whale) by its crews due

▼88

to its large size. This is an R-17 of the Polish LWP. There are a number of different variants of the MAZ-543 chassis with this system. This particular launcher vehicle, with the hydraulic cylinders on the launcher arms, is peculiar to Soviet and Polish units.

88. The SS-23 Spider (Soviet designation: OTR-23) was

intended as a replacement for the Scud. Although a small number entered service in the mid-1980s, they are being withdrawn and dismantled under the terms of the INF treaty.

89. The heavier counterpart of the Scud is the SS-12 Scaleboard. The SS-12

Scaleboard is slated for destruction under the terms of the 1987 INF Treaty signed by the USA and the USSR. This is the only photograph ever released of the SS-12b Scaleboard Mod 2, known to the Russians as the OTR-22.

90. Probably the most famous of the recent Soviet mobile missiles is the SS-20 Saber, called RSD-10 Pioner by the Russians. It is not in Soviet Ground Forces service, but equips special missile regiments of the Soviet RVSN (Strategic Missile Force). It is a large, solid-fuelled intermediate-range missile mounted on a large 12x12 chassis.

91. The SS-20 has been the subject of a considerable controversy, eventually leading to the 1987 INF Treaty between the USA and the USSR which will lead to a ban on this class of missile. This side view gives some idea of the size of the system. The transporter vehicle alone weighs more than 40 tons, plus a further 40 tons for the missile itself.

89 ▲   90 ▼

91 ▼

The *Fotofax* series

A new range of pictorial studies of military subjects for the modeller, historian and enthusiast. Each title features a carefully-selected set of photographs plus a data section of facts and figures on the topic covered. With line drawings and detailed captioning, every volume represents a succinct and valuable study of the subject. New and forthcoming titles:

Warbirds
F-111 Aardvark
P-47 Thunderbolt
B-52 Stratofortress
Stuka!
Jaguar
US Strategic Air Power:
  Europe 1942–1945
Dornier Bombers
RAF in Germany

Vintage Aircraft
German Naval Air Service
Sopwith Camel
Fleet Air Arm, 1920–1939
German Bombers of WWI

Soldiers
World War One: 1914
World War One: 1915
World War One: 1916
Union Forces of the American
  Civil War
Confederate Forces of the
  American Civil War
Luftwaffe Uniforms
British Battledress 1945–1967
  (2 vols)

Warships
Japanese Battleships, 1897–
  1945
Escort Carriers of World War
  Two
German Battleships, 1897–
  1945
Soviet Navy at War, 1941–1945
US Navy in World War Two,
  1943–1944
US Navy, 1946–1980 (2 vols)
British Submarines of World
  War One

Military Vehicles
The Chieftain Tank
Soviet Mechanized Firepower
  Today
British Armoured Cars since
  1945
NATO Armoured Fighting
  Vehicles
The Road to Berlin
NATO Support Vehicles

The *Illustrated* series

The internationally successful range of photo albums devoted to current, recent and historic topics, compiled by leading authors and representing the best means of obtaining your own photo archive.

Warbirds
US Spyplanes
USAF Today
Strategic Bombers, 1945–1985
Air War over Germany
Mirage
US Naval and Marine Aircraft
  Today
USAAF in World War Two
B-17 Flying Fortress
Tornado
Junkers Bombers of World War
  Two
Argentine Air Forces in the
  Falklands Conflict
F-4 Phantom Vol II
Army Gunships in Vietnam
Soviet Air Power Today
F-105 Thunderchief
Fifty Classic Warbirds
Canberra and B-57
German Jets of World War Two

Vintage Warbirds
The Royal Flying Corps in
  World War One
German Army Air Service in
  World War One
RAF between the Wars
The Bristol Fighter
Fokker Fighters of World War
  One
Air War over Britain, 1914–
  1918
Nieuport Aircraft of World War
  One

Tanks
Israeli Tanks and Combat
  Vehicles
Operation Barbarossa
Afrika Korps
Self-Propelled Howitzers
British Army Combat Vehicles
  1945 to the Present
The Churchill Tank
US Mechanized Firepower
  Today
Hitler's Panzers
Panzer Armee Afrika
US Marine Tanks in World War
  Two

Warships
The Royal Navy in 1980s
The US Navy Today
NATO Navies of the 1980s
British Destroyers in World
  War Two
Nuclear Powered Submarines
Soviet Navy Today
British Destroyers in World
  War One
The World's Aircraft Carriers,
  1914–1945
The Russian Convoys, 1941–
  1945
The US Navy in World War
  Two
British Submarines in World
  War Two
British Cruisers in World War
  One
U-Boats of World War Two
Malta Convoys, 1940–1943

Uniforms
US Special Forces of World
  War Two
US Special Forces 1945 to the
  Present
The British Army in Northern
  Ireland
Israeli Defence Forces, 1948 to
  the Present
British Special Forces, 1945 to
  Present
US Army Uniforms Europe,
  1944–1945
The French Foreign Legion
Modern American Soldier
Israeli Elite Units
US Airborne Forces of World
  War Two
The Boer War
The Commandos World War
  Two to the Present
Victorian Colonial Wars

A catalogue listing these series and other Arms & Armour Press titles is available on request from: Sales Department, Arms & Armour Press, Artillery House, Artillery Row, London SW1P 1RT.